Study Guide

Jesus Begins His Ministry to Defeat Sin and Evil

Distribute before session 1 for use in session 1.
Use enrichment magazine pp. 2-4.

Mark 1:1–1:28

Resources for Worship

Use these resources for your daily study at home and at the week's assembly.

Hymn

By all Your saints in warfare,
For all Your saints at rest,
Your holy name, O Jesus,
Forevermore be blest!
For You have won the battle
That they might wear the crown;
And now they shine in glory
Reflected from Your throne.

For Mark, O Lord, we praise You,
The weak by grace made strong,
Whose labors and whose Gospel
Enrich our triumph song.
May we, in all our weakness,
Reflect Your servant life
And follow in Your footsteps,
Enduring cross and strife.

Then let us praise the Father
And worship God the Son
And sing to God the Spirit,
Eternal Three in One,
Till all the ransomed number
Fall down before the throne,
Ascribing pow'r and glory
And praise to God alone.

LSB 518; *TLH* 193

Prayer

O Lord Jesus, bless my study of Your life and ministry as it has been recorded and shared by Your servant St. Mark. Send Your Holy Spirit to guide me into the truth. Thank You for revealing Yourself and Your great love for me. Amen.

Digging Deep
My Personal Study for Week 1

Day 1 • Read Mark 1:1

1. Read verse 1 and Romans 1:16. What power does the Gospel possess?

2. Read Galatians 1:4–9. Is there more than one Gospel?

3. In Galatians 1:6–9, how did Paul look upon so-called "revelations" of divine truth if they did not come from the only source of inspiration and revelation, namely, the God who best revealed Himself in the person and work of Jesus Christ?

4. According to Acts 15:36–40, with which important early Christian leaders did Mark work?

5. Read 2 Timothy 4:11, in what is usually considered to be Paul's last letter. What change is evident in Paul's opinion of Mark?

6. Read 1 Peter 5:13. How close was the relationship between Peter and Mark?

Day 2 • Read Mark 1:2–8

7. Read verses 2–3. What authority was being quoted? (Refer to the cross references in your Bible.)

8. What is the connection between verses 4–8 and verses 2–3?

9. What spiritual realities are connected with the Baptism that John administered (v. 4)? How might these be connected with your Baptism in the name of the triune God?

10. Whom was John the Baptizer talking about in verses 7–8?

Day 3 • Read Mark 1:9–13; Romans 6:3–14

11. John the Baptizer was given the privilege of baptizing Jesus. Who else participated in Jesus' Baptism? Read Mark 1:9–11.

12. Read Romans 6:3–4. Whom does Baptism unite?

13. As St. Paul describes it, what does this union do for the baptized?

14. What do both St. Paul and John the Baptizer call upon the baptized to do? Read Romans 6:5–14.

15. Read Mark 1:12–13. Who opposed Jesus in the wilderness? What does this opposition tell us about Jesus and His character?

Day 4 • Read Mark 1:14–20

16. Read verse 15. What did Jesus teach here about the kingdom of God?

Jesus Heals Those Broken by Sin and Evil

Distribute before session 2 for use in session 2.
Use enrichment magazine pp. 5-7.

Mark 1:29–3:12

Resources for Worship

Use these resources for your daily study at home and at the week's assembly.

Hymn

How sweet the name of Jesus sounds
In a believer's ear!
It soothes our sorrows, heals our wounds,
And drives away our fear.

It makes the wounded spirit whole
And calms the heart's unrest;
'Tis manna to the hungry soul
And to the weary, rest.

O Jesus, shepherd, guardian, friend,
My Prophet, Priest, and King,
My Lord, my life, my way, my end,
Accept the praise I bring.

LSB 524; *LW* 279; *TLH* 364; *EVaS* disk 6, track 23

Prayer

Lord, bless our study of the Gospel of Mark. Let the life, teaching, works, and atoning sacrifice of Jesus impress its life-giving power upon our hearts. Let it strengthen our spirit in faith and love toward You and toward those You have created in Your own image, just like us. Grant that our study might equip us for enhanced service through the works in which You have prepared for us to walk, to Your glory. We ask this in the name of Jesus. Amen.

Digging Deep
My Personal Study for Week 2

Day 1 • Read Mark 1:29–39

1. Which apostle do we know for sure was married? See 1 Corinthians 9:5.

2. What do you think Jesus was showing about Himself when He healed people, whether an individual like Peter's mother-in-law or the crowds who came to Him that evening?

3. Why did Jesus not let the demons speak as He cast them out?

4. The next morning, everyone came looking for Jesus. He told His disciples, "Let us go on to the next towns, that I may preach there also, for that is why I came out" (v. 38). Did Jesus mean that He had gotten up early to get a head start on the trip to the next place? If not, what *did* He mean? Compare Luke 4:43.

5. How can your congregation seek more effectively to keep its focus on its main mission?

Day 2 • Read Mark 1:40–45

6. How does the leper's question express confidence in Jesus?

7. What emotion is ascribed to Jesus in verse 41?

8. What instruction did Jesus give the former leper in verse 44?

9. What is implied in the concepts *clean* and *unclean*? What word would might people use today instead?

10. According to verse 45, what did the man then do? What were the consequences of his actions on Jesus and His ministry?

11. Would you have obeyed the Lord and been silent about His healing? Why or why not? Of course, Jesus has not given *you* this command. Have you been obedient and vocal about your confession of Jesus as Lord and Savior?

Day 3 • Read Mark 2:1–12

12. What problem did the friends of the paralytic encounter? What did they do about it?

13. What problem of the paralytic did Jesus address first?

14. What problem did the scribes have? How did Jesus address it?

15. Which *is* easier to say: "your sins are forgiven" or "rise . . . and walk"? Why did Jesus do what He did in this situation?

16. *Discuss.* The art of Christian living is to believe without seeing; that is, to fasten in faith upon what the Lord says, especially when He forgives our sins, although evidence of this forgiveness may not be found.

Day 4 • Read Mark 2:13–22

17. Whom does Jesus call to ministry in this section? Read Matthew 9:9–13. What was the other name by which this man was called? If you had to guess to which of the twelve tribes of Israel he probably belonged, which would it be?

Jesus Reveals God's Truth

Distribute before session 3 for use in session 3.
Use enrichment magazine pp. 8-10.

Mark 3:13–4:34

Resources for Worship

Use these resources for your daily study at home and at the week's assembly.

Hymn

Almighty God, Your Word is cast
Like seed into the ground;
Now let the dew of heav'n descend
And righteous fruits abound.

Let not the sly satanic foe
This holy seed remove,
But give it root in ev'ry heart
To bring forth fruits of love.

Let not the world's deceitful cares
The rising plant destroy,
But let it yield a hundredfold
The fruits of peace and joy.

LSB 577; *LW* 342; *TLH* 49

Prayer

Dear God, You know all things and have all wisdom. Thank You for revealing the truth about Your love for us. Teach us Your ways and open our eyes to the truth. We pray in the name of the One who is the way, the truth, and the life. Amen.

Digging Deep
My Personal Study for Week 3

Day 1 • Read Mark 3:13–21

1. Read verses 13–15. How many apostles did Jesus appoint, and what did He intend to do with them?

2. Compare verses 16–19 with Matthew 10:2–4 and Luke 6:14–16 (You may want to use a special Bible study tool called a "Harmony of the Gospels.") Which disciple is named first in each list? Which is always named last? Why do you think two disciples are consistently placed first and last?

3. A short phrase gives information about Judas (v. 19). What does this information do for the reader?

4. What makes a list of names interesting to read, not boring? Why is this list of names included here?

5. Read verse 21. What did Jesus' family say about Him at this point in His life? What might have led to this evaluation?

Day 2 • Read Mark 3:22–30

6. Read verse 22. The scribes criticized Jesus. Where did they come from?

7. With whom did these scribes associate Jesus?

8. Read verse 23. What method did Jesus use to speak to the scribes?

9. Read verse 25. Do you know which famous United States senator (later president) used this quotation from Jesus when speaking about strife within the nation? (You may find help from an Internet search engine or a book of quotations.) What was this person trying to save? Jesus was also engaged in a saving effort. What was He working to save?

10. Read verses 28–29. What is the unforgivable sin? Why is it unforgivable compared with others sins?

Day 3 • Read Mark 3:31–35

11. Which of Jesus' family members tried to send for Him? Did Jesus go with His family? What do you think was the reason for this decision?

12. Who is absent from the list of family mentioned here? Why, do you suppose?

13. Read John 19:26–27. Note the responsibility Jesus felt for His mother and the task He assigned the beloved disciple, John. Why might Jesus not assume that His brothers would take care of Mary?

14. Read verse 35. What does Jesus want from those who are in a close relationship with Him?

Day 4 • Read Mark 4:1–20

15. Read verses 3–8. What brings different outcomes for the sower?

16. Read verses 10–13. What did Jesus say about why He speaks in parables? Is this what you would have expected Him to say about the reason for teaching in parables?

17. Read verse 12. What part of the Old Testament is Jesus quoting? (You may want to use a study Bible with cross references or a biblical concordance.) What is the significance of Jesus quoting the Old Testament to make His points?

Jesus Reveals Himself through Signs and Wonders

Distribute before session 4 for use in session 4.
Use enrichment magazine pp. 11-13.

Mark 4:35–5:43

Resources for Worship

Use these resources for your daily study at home and at the week's assembly.

Hymn

O love, how deep, how broad, how high,
Beyond all thought and fantasy,
That God, the Son of God, should take
Our mortal form for mortals' sake!

For us baptized, for us He bore
His holy fast and hungered sore;
For us temptation sharp He knew;
For us the tempter overthrew.

All glory to our Lord and God
For love so deep, so high, so broad;
The Trinity whom we adore
Forever and forevermore.

LSB 544; *LW* 275

Prayer

Good and gracious God, You have all power in heaven and on earth. With You, nothing is impossible. Help me remember that I can always trust You to keep Your promises, no matter how bad things seem to be. Hear me for Jesus' sake. Amen.

Digging Deep
My Personal Study for Week 1

Day 1 • Read Mark 4:35–41

1. What caused the disciples to become fearful in verses 37–38? Have you ever been in a comparable situation?

2. Reread Mark 1:16–19. What line of work had several of Jesus' disciples pursued before He called them to join Him? How does this show the intensity of the crisis in 4:35–41?

3. Read verse 38. What quality of Jesus were the disciples questioning?

4. Read verse 40. What caused Jesus' disappointment in His disciples? Why is this so important to Jesus?

Day 2 • Read Mark 5:1–14

5. Why would the Gerasene people try to put in chains the man with the unclean spirits?

6. What reaction could normally be anticipated toward someone who was able to restore a member of the community who could not successfully be kept in chains?

7. Who seemed to do the speaking for the demons (vv. 7–12)?

8. What do the words that the demons spoke to Jesus show about His superiority to them?

9. What happened to the pigs? What does this show about demons?

Day 3 • Read Mark 5:15–20

10. Read Leviticus 11:7–8. How were the Jews to view pigs?

11. Read verse 15. What emotion did the people feel? What do you think produced that particular emotion?

12. Put yourself in the place of Jesus. How would you react to the request made by the people after the healing of the demon-possessed man?

13. In view of the request of the people, what might have caused Jesus to give the healed man an instruction so different than the one He gave to the healed leper in Mark 1:44?

Day 4 • Read Mark 5:21–34

14. Read verses 22–23. What is happening in these verses? What attracted the attention of Jesus to this situation?

15. Read verses 24–27. What shift of focus occurs in the text?

16. How long had the woman suffered from her affliction? Why is this detail important?

17. How did this woman's healing differ from the other healing miracles that we have already encountered in Mark?

Jesus Is Opposed, Rejected, and Misunderstood

Distribute before session 5 for use in session 5.
Use enrichment magazine pp. 14-16.

Mark 6:1–8:26

Resources for Worship

Use these resources for your daily study at home and at the week's assembly.

Hymn

In Adam we have all been one,
One huge rebellious man;
We all have fled that evening voice
That sought us as we ran.

We fled Thee, and in losing Thee
We lost our brother too;
Each singly sought and claimed his own;
Each man his brother slew.

But Thy strong love, it sought us still
And sent Thine only Son
That we might hear His Shepherd's voice
And, hearing Him, be one.

LSB 569; *LW* 292

Prayer

Lord Jesus, You warned Your disciples that as the world rejects You it also rejects anyone who follows You. When I fear I am losing the battle, remind me that You have already won the war. In my life with You, You have made me more than a conqueror! I praise and thank You for being my strength and my shield. Amen.

Digging Deep
My Personal Study for Week 1

Day 1 • Read Mark 6:1–29

1. According to verses 1–6, what kind of reception did Jesus get in His hometown of Nazareth?

2. Read verses 5–6. What hindered Jesus from bringing more blessings to His hometown? What can we learn from this "negative example"?

3. Read verses 12–13. What three things were done by the Twelve? How do these compare with what Jesus Himself had been doing?

4. Read verses 14–29. How did John the Baptizer die? Why did this happen?

5. Why do you think John the Baptizer's faithfulness was not rewarded with more years of life on earth? What comfort remains ours as Christians in any case?

Day 2 • Read Mark 6:30–6:56

6. Read verses 31–32. What appears to have been Jesus' original intention in going to a desolate place? What might it suggest to us for our planning in life?

7. What motivated Jesus to change His original plan?

8. Read verse 38. Why do you think that Jesus asked the question in this verse? See John 6:6.

9. Think creatively. How could Jesus have addressed the same problem with a different kind of miracle? If you wish, you may suggest why He did what He did instead of something else.

10. Read verses 48 and 51–52. What did Jesus do in this situation?

Day 3 • Read Mark 7:1–23

11. In what respect did the Pharisees criticize Jesus' disciples?

12. Read verses 6–9. What was wrong with the teaching of the Pharisees?

13. Read verses 10–13. What specific problem does Jesus speak of in these verses?

14. Read verses 15–23. What causes a person to be defiled?

15. Compare and contrast the way Jesus instructs people to deal with defilement with the instruction of the Pharisees.

Day 4 • Read Mark 7:24–8:10

16. Read 7:27. How do you think you would react to the kind of response Jesus gave the Syrophoenician woman? Why?

17. Why did Jesus probably respond as He did?

18. What quality or qualities were displayed by the Syrophoenician woman?

Jesus Is Confessed and Reveals His Divinity

Distribute before session 6 for use in session 6.
Use enrichment magazine pp. 17-19.

Mark 8:27–9:13

Resources for Worship

Use these resources for your daily study at home and at the week's assembly.

Hymn

'Tis good, Lord, to be here!
Thy glory fills the night;
Thy face and garments, like the sun,
Shine with unborrowed light.

'Tis good, Lord, to be here,
Thy beauty to behold
Where Moses and Elijah stand,
Thy messengers of old.

Fulfiller of the past
And hope of things to be,
We hail Thy body glorified
And our redemption see.

LSB 414; *LW* 89; *TLH* 135

Prayer

Dear God, You have shone forth Your glory to humankind, especially in the person and work of Your Son, Jesus Christ. In our darkest moments, cause us to remember that You have given us the One who is the light of the world and that there is no darkness He cannot overcome. Hear me for His sake. Amen.

Digging Deep
My Personal Study for Week 1

Day 1 • Read Mark 8:27–30

1. Read verse 27 and Matthew 16:13. What difference is there between the ways Jesus designated Himself in the two accounts? Do the terms mean the same thing?

2. Read verse 28 and 6:14–20. Mark reports that at least one person suggested that Jesus was John the Baptizer. Who suggested this? Are you surprised that this particular person held this belief? Why or why not?

3. Read verse 28 and 2 Kings 2:9–12. What happened to Elijah that made him a popular choice as someone whom the Lord might have brought back as a prophet?

4. Read verse 28 and Malachi 4:5. How might Malachi's prophecy have given people another reason to consider identifying Jesus with Elijah?

5. Read verses 27 and 29. What is the difference between Jesus' two questions? How do the answers to Jesus' questions differ?

Day 2 • Read Mark 8:31–33

6. Read verse 31 and Daniel 7:13–14. What is the difference between the tone and content of these two passages regarding the "Son of Man"?

7. Read verse 31 and Isaiah 53:3–10. In what way did Isaiah supply a "blueprint" for the suffering of the Messiah? Where did Isaiah hint at the resurrection of the Messiah?

8. Read verse 31 and Hosea 6:1–2. In what way do these passages speak in common regarding God's action on a third day?

9. Read Matthew 16:17–19. If Mark's Gospel reflects the preaching of Saint Peter, as Early Church sources have indicated, what might be the reason why Mark's Gospel omitted the information found in this parallel passage from Matthew?

Day 3 • Read Mark 8:34–9:1

10. Read 8:31 and 34. What extra detail does Jesus mention in verse 34 about the manner of His death? How did Jesus know this?

11. Read 8:35. What is the folly of trying to save one's own life? Who alone has the power to give life?

12. Read 8:36. What is the answer to the question posed by Jesus?

13. Read 9:1. What do you think Jesus means regarding the kingdom of God coming with power?

Day 4 • Read Mark 9:2–8

14. Read verse 2 and 14:33. Who belonged to the "inner circle" of the disciples of Jesus? What might have been the reason for Jesus not to share these times with all of the Twelve?

15. Read verses 2–3 and Isaiah 6:1–2. What is described in detail in these two visions of the glory of the Lord? What is—perhaps unexpectedly—not mentioned in detail?

16. Read verses 4–5. Who joined Jesus and His disciples on the mountain? The text does not say how they were recognized. How do you think they may have become known to the disciples and/or to St. Mark the evangelist?

Jesus Teaches about Life Both Now and Forever

Distribute before session 7 for use in session 7.
Use enrichment magazine pp. 23-25.

Mark 9:14–10:52

Resources for Worship

Use these resources for your daily study at home and at the week's assembly.

Hymn

The Law of God is good and wise
And sets His will before our eyes,
Shows us the way of righteousness,
And dooms to death when we transgress.

Its light of holiness imparts
The knowledge of our sinful hearts
That we may see our lost estate
And turn from sin before too late.

To those who help in Christ have found
And would in works of love abound
It shows what deeds are His delight
And should be done as good and right.

To Jesus we for refuge flee,
Who from the curse has set us free,
And humbly worship at His throne,
Saved by His grace through faith alone.

LSB 579; *LW* 329; *TLH* 295; *EVaS* disk 5, track 13

Prayer

Lord Jesus, You are the Good Shepherd, and You lead me safely to a wonderful destination that You have prepared for me. You nourish me and protect me. Help me to embrace Your commandments with joy. When the devil suggests that You are holding out on me, cause me to remember again that You have always been truthful and that he has always been a liar. Amen.

Digging Deep
My Personal Study for Week 1

Day 1 • Read Mark 9:14–29

1. Read verse 22. What was the goal of the demon in regard to the boy? How is this similar to the demons and the pigs in 5:13? What does it suggest about the intent of demons?

2. Read verses 23–24. What belief can accomplish such great things? What must be believed? (Answer this last question based on the entire Bible or at least the Gospel of Mark up to this point.)

3. Read verses 28–29. What did the disciples need to do to cast out demons? Where does this suggest that the real power to cast out demons resides?

4. Why is it surprising that the disciples were having problems casting out a demon? See 3:15. Keep track of the "denseness" of the disciples throughout this week's readings.

Day 2 • Read Mark 9:30–41

5. Read verses 31–32. What do you think hindered the disciples from understanding what Jesus said?

6. Read verses 33–34. Why, in your opinion, did the disciples not want to tell Jesus what they had been discussing?

7. Read verse 35. How did Jesus practice what He preached in this verse?

8. Read verse 37 and Matthew 25:45. How are these statements similar?

9. Read verses 38–40. What are the disciples not to control?

Day 3 • Read Mark 9:42–10:16

10. Read 9:47. What reality does Jesus want people to face about this world as compared to life after this world comes to an end? Which is more important?

11. Read 9:42–50. How does Jesus describe hell? How does this picture go beyond "fire and brimstone"?

12. In 9:42–50, why does Jesus talk about hell? Consider whom He is addressing.

13. Read 10:6–9 and Genesis 2:24. What authoritative word of interpretation does Jesus add to the Genesis passage He quotes? What does it suggest about marriage?

14. Read 10:11–12. Jesus is speaking against the position of the Pharisees on divorce, which was more permissive than that of Jesus. Why might they have wanted to contrast their position with that of Jesus?

15. Read 10:13–16. What is the difference in attitude between the disciples and Jesus? Suggest a reason why this could be the case.

Day 4 • Read Mark 10:17–34

16. Read verse 19. Which commandments does Jesus cover in His recital of the Law? Which did He not include? Offer a suggestion as to why.

Jesus Comes to Jerusalem to Begin His Way to the Cross

Distribute before session 8 for use in session 8.
Use enrichment magazine pp. 26-29.

Mark 11:1–14:52

Resources for Worship

Use these resources for your daily study at home and at the week's assembly.

Hymn

Go to dark Gethsemane,
All who feel the tempter's pow'r;
Your Redeemer's conflict see,
Watch with Him one bitter hour;
Turn not from His griefs away;
Learn from Jesus Christ to pray.

Follow to the judgment hall,
View the Lord of life arraigned;
Oh, the wormwood and the gall!
Oh, the pangs His soul sustained!
Shun not suff'ring, shame, or loss;
Learn from Him to bear the cross.

Calv'ry's mournful mountain climb;
There, adoring at His feet,
Mark that miracle of of time,
God's own sacrifice complete.
"It is finished!" hear Him cry;
Learn from Jesus Christ to die.

Early hasten to the tomb
Where they laid His breathless clay;
All is solitude and gloom.
Who has taken Him away?
Christ is ris'n! He meets our eyes.
Savior, teach us so to rise.

LSB 436; *LW* 110; *TLH* 159; *EVaS* disk 3, track 19

Prayer

Lord Jesus, You knowingly faced suffering and death to rescue me from the penalty for my sins. Give me the resolve to trust You and follow You wherever You would have me go, ready to experience whatever I must in the sure hope that You will use Your almighty power to make all things work for good in the end. I believe that You have secured for me a place of eternal bliss. I trust that You will get me through all things to reach the destination You have appointed for me in Your grace. Amen.

Digging Deep
My Personal Study for Week 1

Day 1 • Read Mark 11:1–33

1. Read verses 8–10. Why do you think Jesus was welcomed as He was?

2. Read verses 12–14, 20–25 and Jeremiah 24. What fruit do these passages have in common? What seems to be symbolized by the fruit?

3. Read verses 15–19, 27–33. What is it that Jesus assumed authority to do?

4. In verses 27–33, how does Jesus respond to the question put forth to Him by the chief priests, scribes, and elders?

5. What kinds of things might Jesus cleanse from today's churches?

Day 2 • Read Mark 12:1–44

6. Read verses 1–12. What does Jesus reveal in verse 8?

7. Read Psalm 118:22–23. What is symbolized by the stone in Mark 12:10?

8. Read verses 13–27. What is the motive behind the questions asked of Jesus in verses 14 and 23? Were the questioners seeking spiritual guidance?

9. Read verses 28–34. If you were forced to summarize the Law of God in a single word, what would that word be? Why?

10. Read verses 41–44. What is it that God treasures in offerings?

Day 3 • Read Mark 13:1–37

11. Read verse 2. Has this prophecy of Jesus been fulfilled? How has it or will it be fulfilled?

12. What "end" did Jesus refer to in verse 7?

13. Are the things that Jesus described in verses 14–23 good things to look forward to? Compare with 8:36. What should our attitude be toward suffering in this world?

14. Read verse 32. Jesus spoke of the future with many detailed predictions, but what information was He not in a position to supply?

15. In light of His teachings in these passages, what advice does Jesus give to His followers in verse 33?

Day 4 • Read Mark 14:1–25

16. Read verse 1. What was in the hearts of the chief priests and scribes? Should this seem strange?

17. Of what fact does Jesus show awareness in verse 8?

Jesus Is Crucified and Resurrected according to God's Plan

Distribute before session 9 for use in session 9.
Use enrichment magazine pp. 30-32.

Mark 14:53–16:8

Resources for Worship

Use these resources for your daily study at home and at the week's assembly.

Hymn

"Speak, Mary, declaring
What you saw when wayfaring."
"The tomb of Christ, who is living,
The glory of Jesus' resurrection;
Bright angels attesting,
The shroud and napkin resting.
My Lord, my hope, is arisen;
To Galilee He goes before you."

Were Christ not arisen,
Then death were still our prison.
Now, with Him to life restored,
We praise the Father of our Lord. Alleluia!

"Christians to the Pascal Victim," and *"Christ Is Arisen"*
LSB 460, st. 2; 459, st. 2; *LW* 10

Prayer

Lord Jesus, I thank You for the salvation You have provided for me at such a great cost. As I study Your betrayal, Passion, death, and resurrection, work in me a deeper appreciation for the love You have displayed for me in Your great sacrifice. Amen.

Digging Deep
My Personal Study for Week 1

Day 1 • Read Mark 14:53–72

1. Read verses 55–56. What problems are obvious about this "trial" of Jesus? What is wrong with the process and procedure?

2. Compare verse 58 with John 2:19–22. How did Jesus' accusers misuse His words?

3. Read verses 61–63. What did Jesus say that caused the high priest to take offense?

4. Read verse 64 together with Leviticus 24:16. Of what did the high priest say Jesus was guilty? What was the prescribed penalty?

5. Read John 18:15–18. What extra information does this passage supply?

Day 2 • Read Mark 15:1–20

6. How does the charge on which Jesus was condemned by Pilate differ from the charge of which He was convicted by the Council?

7. What seems to be the reason why Pilate offers the crowd a choice between Jesus and Barabbas?

8. Read Acts 3:14. This passage alludes to Barabbas. Whom is Luke quoting in this passage? (Remember who has been suggested as the key source to Mark for his Gospel.)

9. What may have motivated the Roman soldiers to mock Jesus?

Day 3 • Read Mark 15:21–41

10. Read verse 21. Why would Simon of Cyrene have been identified as the father of Alexander and Rufus? See Romans 16:13.

11. Read Psalm 22:1–8, 14–18. What is the significance of this psalm? How does it connect with Mark's account of Jesus' crucifixion?

12. Read Hebrews 10:19–22. What incident in Mark 15 might this passage allude to?

13. Read verse 39. What did the centurion say? Who else has said this in the Gospel of Mark? Who has not said it?

14. What do all the witnesses of the crucifixion of Jesus mentioned in verses 40–41 have in common?

Day 4 • Read Mark 15:42–47

15. What does Mark call the day on which Jesus died? Which day of the week was it?

16. What group did Joseph of Arimathea belong to?

17. Read Matthew 27:57, 60 and Luke 23:50–51. What additional information about Joseph is found in these passages?

18. What did Joseph buy for Jesus?

19. Who witnessed where the body of Jesus was interred? Why is this important?

Day 5 • *Read Mark 16:1–8*

20. Compare Mark's account with that in Matthew 28:2–7. Whom did the women find in the tomb instead of Jesus? Can these accounts be harmonized?

21. Read verse 6. What declaration is made regarding Jesus?

22. Why do you think that Peter is singled out among the Eleven in verse 7?

23. Compare verse 7 with 14:28. When and where had Jesus said He would go before them to Galilee after His resurrection?

24. Most study Bibles and modern Bible translations offer a note about the verses following verse 8. What is said about these verses?

18. Read verse 19. What does the disciples' question show about their confidence in themselves? Read verse 29. How does Peter's response contrast with that of his fellow disciples?

19. In light of verse 21, where can we be virtually sure that Judas is spending eternity?

20. Read verse 24 and Matthew 26:28. What helpful detail does Matthew's account include?

Day 5 • Read Mark 14:26–52

21. Read verse 33. Whom did Jesus invite to join Him as He goes to Gethsemane to pray? Does this appear to be a random selection?

22. Read verses 35–36. Which attribute of God did Jesus explicitly mention in His prayer?

23. How did the disciples of Jesus disappoint Him?

24. Read verse 47 and Luke 22:50–51. What information does Luke uniquely provide at this point? Why is it especially appropriate that Luke was the evangelist to share this information?

25. Read verse 47 and John 18:10. What information does John share that one would not know from the account of Mark (or Matthew or Luke)? Why might Mark have omitted this information?

17. Read verses 21–23 and 9:45. What do both of these passages have in common?

18. In times past, some Christians read or heard Jesus' words to the rich young man, sold all they had, and took up monastic life. Does Jesus want all Christians to do this?

19. Read verse 27. What is contrasted in this verse?

20. Read verses 33–34. What does Jesus know is awaiting Him in Jerusalem?

Day 5 • Read Mark 10:35–52

21. What is wrong with what James and John say to Jesus in verse 35? What would have been better to say?

22. How do verses 35–45 compare with 9:33–37? How are these passages alike, and how are they different?

23. Compare verses 35–39 with Matthew 20:20–22. What is the big difference between these passages? What might account for this difference?

24. Read verse 47 and 2 Samuel 7:8, 12–13. By which title is Jesus addressed? What is the significance of this title?

25. Summarize the instances in which the disciples showed themselves to be "dense" in this week's readings from Mark.

17. Read verse 7. Where else did a voice from heaven declare much the same message? (You may wish to use cross-references or a concordance for this question.)

18. What is the significance of the event and the special Old Testament dignitaries encountered by Jesus and the three disciples? Why do you suppose these two particular individuals were chosen instead of others from the Old Testament?

Day 5 • Read Mark 9:9–13

19. Read verse 9. When could the disciples who were on the mountain with Jesus testify about what they had seen? What might have been the reason for this instruction?

20. Read verse 12. On which aspect of the Messiah's work did Jesus focus His disciples' attention?

21. Read verse 13 and Matthew 17:12–13. What extra explanation does Matthew provide regarding the intended sense of God's prophecies about the return of Elijah?

22. Read 2 Peter 1:16–18. What did Peter himself highlight about the transfiguration?

23. Read 1 Kings 19:1–10. Who troubled Elijah for doing the will of the Lord?

24. Who troubled the "Elijah" of whom Jesus speaks in verse 13, also for doing the Lord's will?

25. What do the troublemakers mentioned in questions 24 and 25 have in common?

19. Read 8:4. What might surprise people about the question of the disciples? Why?

20. What does the question in 8:4 reveal about the disciples' relationship to Jesus?

21. Read 8:9. How many does Jesus feed in this instance?

Day 5 • Read Mark 8:11–26

22. Read verse 11. What kind of attitude did the Pharisees have as they talked with Jesus? By implication, how were they rating themselves in comparison with Jesus?

23. What did the Pharisees seek from Jesus?

24. Who should have been testing whom?

25. Read verse 15. What is the leaven or yeast of the Pharisees? What attribute of leaven or yeast did Jesus use to make His point?

26. Read Exodus 12:15. Why were people there told to beware of leaven or yeast?

18. Read verse 34. What quality does Jesus say brought about the healing for the woman? Contrast the woman with those who lacked this quality in the section of Mark under consideration earlier this week.

Day 5 • Read Mark 5:35–43

19. Jesus had been interrupted in His attention to Jairus's daughter. What was the interruption?

20. Do you always remember to finish things when you are distracted by an interruption? Jesus remembered! What does this tell us about Him?

21. Read verse 35. What had taken place during the interim between the time that Jesus first started out to help Jairus's daughter and the event in this verse?

22. Read verse 40. Why did the people laugh at Jesus?

23. Think of another time when Jesus healed someone after arriving "too late." What was it?

24. **Challenge Question**. Not only are these miracles of Jesus striking but so also is His timing in performing them. Review the timing of the miracles in Mark 4:35–5:43. What do you learn from Christ's timing for your own life?

18. Read verse 14. What is sown in the parable of the sower? That is, what spiritual reality is represented by the seed?

19. Read verse 15. Who works to steal away what is sown? Why?

Day 5 • Read Mark 4:21–34

20. Read verse 21. What is the obvious answer to Jesus' question? Why does Jesus make His point by asking a question? Did Jesus often employ this way of making a point?

21. What "light" do you think Jesus is speaking of in verse 22? See John 1:4–5; 8:12; 2 Corinthians 4:6.

22. Read verses 26–29. Is it possible that the word *seed* should be understood in this parable as it was in Mark 4:14? If so, who makes the seed grow?

23. Read verses 30–32. Who makes the seed grow in this parable?

24. What is the basic point of the parable of the mustard seed (vv. 30–32)?

25. Read verse 34. What special instruction did the disciples get over and above the crowds?

18. What assets and liabilities might this man have been able to bring from his old job experience to his new position as a disciple and apostle?

19. Read verse 17. Do you suppose Jesus really thought that the Pharisees and scribes were righteous? Do you think the scribes thought they were righteous? Do you think the scribes thought that Jesus thought they were righteous?

20. What did the Pharisees want Jesus to explain in verses 18–19? How did Jesus respond?

Day 5 • Read Mark 2:23–3:12

21. What is the significance of the day in question in 2:23–28 and 3:1–6?

22. What is Jesus' understanding of this day's significance? How does His understanding compare with that of the Pharisees?

23. What is revealed about the attitude of the Pharisees toward Jesus in 3:6?

24. Read Colossians 2:16–17. Relate Paul's statement to Mark 2:23–3:5.

25. How does one keep the Third Commandment today?

17. Because God's reign is here, what did Jesus want to occur?

18. Read verses 16–18. What was the "carryover" to which Jesus alluded as these fishermen would become apostles? How were their "tools" going to change with their new "trade"?

19. Notice that these fishermen had been using nets, not a line and pole, when Jesus spoke of their future of catching men. What might the Church today learn from this fact as it continues to "fish for men"? In other words, how can we make sure that our fishing for men more resembles net-fishing than line-and-pole fishing?

Day 5 • Read Mark 1:21–28

20. Look at verses 10, 12, 18, 20, 21, and 23 of chapter 1. Which word is used repeatedly? (Mark uses this word a lot!)

21. Besides ordering a demon to come out of a man, what else did Jesus tell the demon to do? Why do you think He did this?

22. What distinguished the teaching of Jesus from that of the scribes? See verses 22 and 27.

23. Today the Church and her pastors have a ministry of "Word and Sacrament." How does this resemble the early days of Jesus' own ministry, as shown in Mark 1?

24. **Challenge Question.** The Sacraments fight the demonic! How do they do this, and how is this fact of comfort to you?

Study Guide

The Church Is Prepared for Pentecost

Distribute before session 1 for use in session 1.
Use enrichment magazine pp. 2–4.

Acts 1

Resources for Worship

Use these resources for your daily study at home and at the week's assembly.

Hymn

O Holy Spirit, enter in,
And in our hearts Your work begin,
And make our hearts Your dwelling.
Sun of the soul, O Light divine,
Around and in us brightly shine
Your strength in us upwelling.
In Your radiance Life from heaven
Now is given Overflowing
Gift of gifts beyond all knowing.

O mighty Rock, O Source of life,
Let Your good Word in doubt and strife
Be in us strongly burning
That we be faithful unto death
And live in love and holy faith,
From You true wisdom learning.
Lord, Your mercy On us shower;
By Your power Christ confessing,
We will cherish all Your blessing.

Michael Schirmer; tr. Catherine Winkworth, adapt.

Something to Think About

On my heart imprint Your image,
Blessed Jesus, king of grace,
That life's riches, cares, and pleasures
Never may Your work erase;
Let the clear inscription be:
Jesus, crucified for me,
Is my life, my hope's foundation,
And my glory and salvation!

Thomas H. Kingo; tr. Peer O. Strömme, alt.

Prayer

Lord Jesus, sometimes I feel so caught,
driven first in one direction and then another.
My time, my life, are so full, so out of control;
I feel swept along, helpless and exhausted.
Then it gets too quiet. The nagging fear resurfaces:
"It's all a waste. There is no purpose. Nothing matters."
Not true!
You lived *for* me. You spent Yourself *for* me.
You died *for* me. You conquered death *for* me.
And planned a purpose for my life too.
These few minutes in the sweep of time count.
You promised. Jesus, live through me, as You promised.
Share the Good News through me, as You promised.
By the power of Your Spirit. Amen.

Digging Deep
My Personal Study for Week 1

Day 1 • Read Acts 1:1–5

1. Compare Luke 1:1–4 and Acts 1:1. The Acts of the Apostles, written by St. Paul's loyal friend Luke, is addressed to Theophilus, a name that in Greek literally means "lover of God." Theophilus may have been a servant of the Roman government and a patron or publisher of Luke's books.

a. How does Luke summarize his first volume (Acts 1:1–3)?

b. What does Acts 1:8 suggest to us about the contents of this second volume?

2. How do the following verses reveal Luke's purpose in writing this account?

Acts 6:7

Acts 9:31

Acts 12:24

3. When Jesus died, the disciples thought they had lost their leader and their source of strength and purpose. Read verses 2–5 and Luke 24:36–49, noting how the resurrected Lord restored the confidence of His disciples and reassured them of their purpose. If you had been there, which words of Jesus would have been most comforting and encouraging to you?

4. Look up the following references to discover information about Luke, the author of this book:

a. Luke 1:3

b. Colossians 4:14

c. Philemon 24

d. 2 Timothy 4:11

Day 2 • Read Acts 1:6–8

Do you ever feel as if you are spinning your wheels and exhausting yourself in the process? In today's reading notice how Jesus' last, loving words to His friends on earth set priorities, give direction, and promise power for His disciples.

5. Judging from their words to Jesus (v. 6), what seems to have been a priority concern of the disciples?

6. *For personal reflection. Sharing optional.* What are the two top priorities (major concerns) in *my* life right now and how do they fit with Jesus' top priority for His disciples, that we be His witnesses (v. 8)?

7. Acts 1:8 is a key verse. What does this verse reveal about Jesus' continuing work on this earth?

8. **Challenge ques tion.** This week jot down your daily activities each evening. Notice how you are spending your time and energy. Which items on your list reflect Jesus' priorities for you? Thank Jesus for the leading of

The Church Is Empowered by the Holy Spirit

Distribute before session 2 for use in session 2.
Use enrichment magazine pp. 8–11.

Acts 2:1–41

Resources for Worship

Use these resources for your daily study at home and at the week's assembly.

Hymn

Creator Spirit, by whose aid
The world's foundations first were laid,
Come, visit ev'ry humble mind;
Come, pour Your joys on humankind;
From sin and sorrow set us free;
May we, each one, Your temple be.

O Source of uncreated light,
The bearer of God's gracious might,
Thrice-holy fount, thrice-holy fire,
Our hearts with heav'nly love inspire;
Refreshing show'rs of blessing bring
To sanctify us as we sing.

Immortal honor, endless fame
Attend the gracious Father's name;
The Savior Son be glorified,
Who for lost man's redemption died;
And equal adoration rise
For You, O Spirit, to the skies.

Rhabanus Manrus; tr. John Dryden, alt.

Something to Think About

"Without the Holy Spirit hearts are either hardened in sins or they despair. But both are contrary to the will of God."

What Luther Says, *ed. Ewald Plass (St. Louis: Concordia Publishing House, 1959), § 2047.*

Prayer

Oh, Holy Spirit, living Fire,
You help me see my sin.
You turn my heart to God, my Father.
You move me to believe. You give me what to say.
What joy I find in Your indwelling!
Blaze brightly in my heart, dear Spirit—
Every day. Amen.

Digging Deep
My Personal Study for Week 2

Day 1 • Read Acts 2:1–13

1. Pentecost (meaning "fiftieth day") was a Jewish harvest festival that fell 50 days after Passover. All males of Israel were required to travel to the temple in Jerusalem for worship (vv. 9–11).

a. How would you imagine the city to be that day?

b. Where were Jesus' followers on this Pentecost?
Acts 2:1

Luke 24:53

c. What were they doing (same verses)?

2. God had set the stage. Within this setting He acted.

a. What were the *outward* visible signs of the Spirit's presence (vv. 2–3)?

b. What did the tongues of *fire* symbolize?
Exodus 3:2

Exodus 13:21

c. What evidenced the Spirit's *inward* presence in the disciples (v. 4)?

d. For what purpose did the Spirit give the apostles the ability to speak in other known, understandable languages (vv. 5, 11)?

3. What significance do you see in the fact that the Holy Spirit touched and filled *each* Christian there?

Acts 2:4

Joel 2:28–32a

Galatians 3:28

4. What evidence is there that the Holy Spirit is living within *you* right now?

Acts 2:38

1 Corinthians 12:3

Romans 14:17

2 Thessalonians 2:13

Day 2 • Read Acts 2:14–21

5. a. Read the following references. What was Peter like before the Pentecost experience?

Matthew 16:21–23

Matthew 26:69–75

John 18:10–11

b. What adjectives would you use to describe Peter in Acts 2:14–21 to refer to the transformation that the Holy Spirit had brought into his life?

6. Read verse 19. In our world today, what events characterized by "blood and fire and billows of smoke" are signs to us of the ultimate day of judgment?

The Church Proclaims the Word with Great Boldness

Distribute before session 3 for use in session 3.
Use enrichment magazine pp. 5–7.

Acts 2:42–4:31

Resources for Worship

Use these resources for your daily study at home and at the week's assembly.

Hymn

Lord God, to You we all give praise,
To You with joy our thanks we raise
For angel multitudes that shine
In Your great throne room crystalline.

From them flow light and heav'nly grace
Reflecting splendors of Your face.
They heed Your voice, they know it well,
In godly wisdom they excel.

Philipp Melanchthon; German tr. Paul Eber;
English tr. Emanuel Cronenwett, alt.

A Word to Ponder

In my anguish I cried to the LORD,
and He answered by setting me free.
The LORD is with me; I will not be afraid.
What can man do to me?
The LORD is with me; He is my helper.
I will look in triumph on my enemies.
It is better to take refuge in the LORD
than to trust in man.
It is better to take refuge in the LORD
than to trust in princes.

Psalm 118:5–9

A Verse to Remember

Salvation is found in no one else, for there is no other name under heaven given to men by which we must be saved. *Acts 4:12*

Prayer

Lord Jesus, You are the only way to the Father.
Thank You for finding me and setting me upon Your path.
When I stumble, when I stray, when I'm scared,
Forgive me and take away my fear.
Link me with my brothers and sisters in Christ.
Forge us into one strong body, fearless in speaking for You.
Amen.

Digging Deep
My Personal Study for Week 3

Day 1 • Read Acts 2:42–47

1. Summarize what is meant by "the apostles' teaching" (v. 42).

Matthew 28:20

Acts 2:22–24, 36, 38–39

2. What do 1 Corinthians 10:16 and 11:24 and Acts 20:7 suggest about the meaning of "breaking of bread" in verse 42?

3. **Challenge question.** "Wonders and miraculous signs" (v. 43) occurred in the earliest days of the church but have not been as apparent since then. What do you think accounts for this?

1 Corinthians 13:8

2 Corinthians 12:12

Hebrews 2:3–4

4. In this picture of life in the early church, what single feature would you rate as the most important for us to emphasize or recapture in our local fellowship of believers today? (As you consider this, pray God the Holy Spirit to enable *you* to be part of renewal in

the church.)

5. a. Note who was responsible for the growth of the church (v. 47). What additional information concerning this do we find in Isaiah 55:10–11?

b. How might this be a source of encouragement to the Lord's church today?

Day 2 • Read Acts 3:1–10

6. Notice that Peter and John continued to go to the temple to pray at the customary hour. Paul also continued to use the temple as a place of worship (Acts 21:26–27). Jewish Christians in Jerusalem continued to use the temple as a place for worship as long as they could. However, how did the importance and significance of the temple change with the completion of the once-for-all sacrifice Christ made on the cross?

Matthew 27:50–51

Hebrews 9:1–5

Hebrews 10:14–22

7. a. Meditate on the wealth of meaning in the name "Jesus Christ of Nazareth" (v. 6). What does the personal name *Jesus* mean in the original language of the Bible (Matthew 1:21)?

b. *Christ*, of course, is not Jesus' "family" or last name, but rather refers to the "office" or position of authority to which God called Him. *Christ* in the original Greek of the New Testament means the same as the Hebrew Old Testament term *Messiah*—"anointed" (with olive oil), signifying appointment to an office (see 1 Samuel 16:1, 13). To what threefold office was Jesus anointed (appointed)?

Deuteronomy 18:15

Hebrews 7:26–27

John 18:36–37

8. Jesus' twofold nature can be seen in the reference to Him as "of Nazareth" (3:6) [true man] and as "the *author* of life" [true God] (3:15). Why is that twofold nature of Jesus so crucially important for our salvation?

John 1:3

Hebrews 2:14

1 Peter 1:18–19

9. *For personal reflection. Sharing optional.* Think of some instance from your own life when, like the beggar before the Gate Beautiful, you received a great blessing that you did not expect. Think back to it. If your first reaction was to thank God, thank Him again now. If that was not your first reaction, thank Him now.

The Church Meets Both Internal and External Challenges

Distribute before session 4 for use in session 4.
Use enrichment magazine pp. 18–20.

Acts 4:32–5:42

Resources for Worship

Use these resources for your daily study at home and at the week's assembly.

Hymn

Christians, while on earth abiding,
Let us never cease to pray,
Firmly in the Lord confiding
As our parents in their day.
Be the children's voices raised
To the God their parents praised.
May his blessing, failing never,
Rest upon His people ever.

Bless us, Father, and protect us
From all harm in all our ways;
Patiently, O Lord, direct us
Safely through these fleeting days.
Let Your face upon us shine,
Fill us with Your peace divine.
Praise the Father, Son, and Spirit!
Praise Him, all who life inherit!

Johan Olof Wallin, st. 1; Jesper Svedberg, st. 2; tr. unknown, adapt.

Something to Think About

There is something we must learn how to do:
it is to begin and end each day, as well as every week,
with celebration.
It would be well if we spent less time with pious consideration of our failures
and more time in celebrating the loving forgiveness
and acceptance that God has already offered to us.

I wonder if there is anything our world is more in need of
than the honest and unrepressed joy of God's children
who truly accept God's gifts of redemption
and reconciliation and who respond to God's eternal
love by lovingly offering their bodies and beings
on the altar of their fellow person's needs.

Leslie F. Brandt, A Battle Manual for Christian Survival *(St. Louis: Concordia Publishing House, 1980), 58–59.*

Prayer

Lord Jesus, Your love astounds me.
So generous You are with mercy; So stingy am I with mine.
Forgive me.
Fill me with love for my fellow believers
That I joyfully, unselfishly respond to their need.
Fill me with love for those outside the family of faith that I fearlessly, effectively tell what You have done for us all. Amen.

Digging Deep
My Personal Study for Week 4

Day 1 • Read Acts 4:32–37

Unity, generosity, and encouragement in carrying out a single, important purpose—all were characteristic of the believers in the early church.

1. Imagine you are a member of this early group of believers. List the priorities of your group. (In other words, what do you and your group think and feel are the most important ways to spend your time and energy until Jesus returns?) Review Acts 2:42–47 and 4:32–35.

2. Continue imagining. What seems to be affecting your choices and priorities now that you have become a part of this group of believers?

3. Sketch a word portrait of Barnabas, one of the group converted to the faith. See the following passages in Acts:

4:36–37

9:26–28

11:19–30

13:1–3

14:21–28

15:36–41

4. a. Who has been a "Barnabas" to you?

b. How has this person encouraged you in your spiritual life? supported you in your physical needs?

c. To whom can you be a "Barnabas" (encourager)?

Day 2 • Read Acts 5:1–11

Luke is painfully honest in presenting his picture of the early church. Barnabas's good example of sharing is realistically balanced with the bad example of Ananias and Sapphira. It is clear the church is not made up of perfect people.

5. a. The members of the Christian community had a right to keep back whatever they chose from the sale of their own property. What, then, was the sin in the deed of Ananias and Sapphira (vv. 2–4, 8)? (See also 1 Samuel 16:7b.)

b. What do you think motivated this couple?

6. Read verse 8. Consider why Peter asked his question of Sapphira. How might the outcome have been different for Sapphira?

7. a. Against whom was their sin committed (vv. 3, 4, 9)?

b. **Challenge question.** Why do you think such severe consequences were laid upon this couple's sin?

Romans 6:23

1 Corinthians 5:6

The Church Has Its First Martyr

Distribute before session 5 for use in session 5.
Use enrichment magazine pp. 26–28.

Acts 6–7

Resources for Worship

Use these resources for your daily study at home and at the week's assembly.

Hymn

Jesus lives! The vict'ry's won!
Death no longer can appall me;
Jesus lives! Death's reign is done!
From the grave will Christ recall me.
Brighter scenes will then commence;
This shall be my confidence.

Jesus lives! For me He died,
Hence will I, to Jesus living,
Pure in heart and act abide,
Praise to Him and glory giving.
All I need God will dispense;
This shall be my confidence.

Jesus lives! And I am sure
Neither life nor death shall sever
Me from Him. I shall endure
In His love, through death, forever.
God will be my sure defense;
This shall be my confidence.

Christian F. Gellert; tr. Frances E. Cox, alt.

Something to Think About

It is time that I who call myself by His name throw out my adulterated concepts of discipleship and become authentic in my Christian life.
This necessitates my going back to His Word and pattern for my life.
There is nothing easygoing about the kind of life and committal that Christ prescribes.
It is costly and demanding.
It promises not softness but suffering,
not comfort but challenge,
not safety but sacrifice.
There is peace; there is also persecution.
There is security, joy, enrichment;
there is also blood, sweat, and tears.

Leslie F. Brandt, A Battle Manual for Christian Survival *(St. Louis: Concordia Publishing House, 1980), 90.*

Prayer

Lord Jesus, have mercy on me, for I have often failed to see what my brothers and sisters see, to understand their viewpoint, to learn of their experiences, to feel their pain. In my own comfortable corner I may think I see things clearly, but I often don't.

Forgive my prejudice, my snap judgments. Help me listen to those who see things differently than I do. Make me be willing to change when necessary. Give all of us Your Spirit to guide us in resolving differences in ways that please You best. Lord Jesus, have mercy on me, for I have often failed to speak up for You when threatened, to stand fast when I'm accused, to tell what You have done, to give You Your credit due.

Too often I'm more concerned about my own comfort than I am about my neighbor's soul. Forgive my selfishness.

Help me speak the Gospel of peace and mercy found only in You and in Your death and resurrection.

Give all of us Your Spirit to guide us in speaking exactly the right words at the right time for Your glory. Amen.

Digging Deep
My Personal Study for Week 5

A considerable length of time may have elapsed between the events recorded in chapter 5 and those in chapter 6. The young church continues to grow. Luke stops keeping count of converts. At this point the church is entirely Jewish. Two groups of Jews comprised the membership: Hebraic Jews were natives of Palestine, spoke Aramaic, and followed Jewish culture and customs; Grecian Jews were born outside Palestine, spoke Greek, and were influenced by Greek attitudes and culture. The Grecian Jews probably came to Jerusalem for Pentecost and stayed on after their conversion to Christ. They were commonly held in contempt by Hebraic Jews, who were prejudiced against anything remotely Gentile. No wonder conflict arose in so large a group with diverse perspectives! In this week's study, note how God guides His church through conflict within and without and turns pain and suffering into blessing.

Day 1 • Read Acts 6:1–7

1. A problem arose within the church. From verses 2–4 find phrases that show how the apostles handled the problem in the following ways.

a. The apostles kept their priorities straight by recognizing and holding to their own calling.

b. The apostles were not self-serving or power-hungry; they involved the entire church in the decision-making process.

c. The apostles knew that spiritual qualifications were essential for service within the church.

2. a. How did the lives of the apostles, the seven helpers, and the whole group of believers reflect the indwelling of the Spirit as they worked through the solution of their problem?

b. How can the principles reflected in questions 1 and 2a apply to believers and congregations today?

3. Acts 6:7 is one of a series of progress reports on the growth of the church and marks the close of the first major division in Acts. What appears most significant to you in this report?

Day 2 • Read Acts 6:8–15

Grecian Jews, such as Stephen and Philip, who believed the Gospel and became Christians, saw its universal implications. Perhaps their contact with the wider world made them open to sharing the Gospel with Gentiles. But Grecian Jews who rejected the Gospel became its bitterest opponents. They were determined to protect their cherished Jewish religious institutions from being undermined by the Gospel's appeal to Gentiles. Conflict was inevitable.

4. a. How does Scripture describe Stephen (Acts 6:5–15)?

b. *For personal reflection. Sharing optional.* Which of Stephen's characteristics need cultivation in your own life?

5. How was Stephen's trial similar to Jesus' trial? (See Mark 14:56–59.)

6. a. What was the heart of the accusations against Stephen (vv. 13–14)?

b. Why would traditional Jews feel especially threatened by Stephen?

c. Change comes hard to people. A common statement is "We've never done it that way before." In your opinion, what areas of church practice should allow for possible change and what areas should not?

The Church Takes the Gospel to Samaria and Beyond

Distribute before session 6 for use in session 6.
Use enrichment magazine pp. 12–14.

Acts 8

Resources for Worship

Use these resources for your daily study at home and at the week's assembly.

Hymn

God, whose almighty word
Chaos and darkness heard
And took their flight:
Hear us, we humbly pray,
And where the Gospel day
Sheds not its glorious ray,
Let there be light!

Lord, who once came to bring,
On Your redeeming wing,
Healing and sight,
Health to the sick in mind,
Sight to the inly blind:
Oh, now to humankind
Let there be light!

John Marriott, alt.

Prayer

Lord Jesus, Your Spirit within me calls You Lord!
Thank You for Your Spirit,
Who called me to faith by the Gospel and who fills me with trust in Your promise to forgive my sins.
Now let Your Spirit move me to see my neighbor's need, to tell what I know is true, to love as I am loved, to face unafraid whatever opposition to Your Gospel lies ahead in my path. In Your name, Jesus, by the power of Your Spirit I pray. Amen.

Digging Deep
My Personal Study for Week 6

Approximately five years have passed since the Day of Pentecost. A new phase of growth is about to begin. What looks like a deterrent, cruel persecution, becomes instead a means of expanding the church.

Day 1 • Read Acts 8:1–3

1. Review Acts 1:1–11 and read Matthew 24:1–14.

a. What phrases in these passages indicate that Jesus clearly is in charge of the growth of the church?

b. What is clearly the Lord's objective before the end? (See also 1 Timothy 2:3–4.)

c. Who is chosen to carry out the Lord's plan?

d. What will hasten the Lord's return (Matthew 24:14)?

2. a. Compare Acts 8:1 to 1:8. In 8:1 what was God using to fulfill Jesus' prediction in 1:8?

b. What instructions had Jesus given His followers for this type of situation (Matthew 10:23)?

3. Not only did Saul (later to be called Paul as he brought the Gospel to the Gentiles after his conversion) approve of Stephen's murder, but also he took the lead in persecuting the believers. The Greek words used in 8:3 picture Saul as a wild animal, attacking and ravaging the church with brutal, sadistic cruelty. What does Paul later (after his conversion) tell us about what motivated his earlier savage behavior?

Philippians 3:5–6

1 Timothy 1:12–14

Day 2 • Read 8:4–13

4. The result of persecution was the spread of the Gospel (Acts 8:4)! The evil intent of Joseph's brothers turned out for his good and theirs (Genesis 50:20)! Think about—and praise God for—a time in your life when God turned your suffering to good for you and/or for the progress of the Gospel.

5. Note what those who were scattered by persecution did in verse 4. What, specifically, do you think these displaced Christians told their new neighbors?

6. Because of persecution, Christians from Jerusalem sought safety in remote areas, probably fleeing first to Samaria. Philip, one of the seven mentioned in Acts 6:5, became an evangelist there. His ministry included miraculous healings, both in the spiritual and physical realms. (See v. 7.) Verse 6 provides an explanation of why God chose to work numerous outstanding miracles during the era of the birth of the Christian church through Philip, Stephen, the apostles, and others. From verses 6, 8, and 12, what was the result of these miracles?

Day 3 • Read Act 8:14–17

7. a. The Samaritans originated from Gentiles who moved into the Holy Land during the exile of the Israelites and intermarried with those Jews who had been left behind in the exile. What was the result (2 Kings 17:24–34, 40–41)?

b. How did the Jews at the time of Jesus and the Book of Acts feel about the Samaritans?

Luke 9:51–55

John 4:9

8. **Challenge question.** a. This section of Acts requires the use of the "Scripture interprets Scripture" principle to avoid confusion regarding the work of the Holy Spirit. The apostles visited the Samaritan believers, who to this point had not experienced any visible out-

The Church Receives an Unlikely Convert

Distribute before session 7 for use in session 7.
Use enrichment magazine pp. 29–32.

Acts 9:1–31

Resources for Worship

Use these resources for your daily study at home and at the week's assembly.

Hymn

Amazing grace! How sweet the sound
That saved a wretch like me!
I once was lost but now am found,
Was blind but now I see!

The Lord has promised good to me,
His word my hope secures;
He will my shield and portion be
As long as life endures.

Through many dangers, toils, and snares
I have already come;
His grace has brought me safe so far,
His grace will see me home.

Yes, when this flesh and heart shall fail
And mortal life shall cease,
Amazing grace shall then prevail
In heaven's joy and peace.

John Newton, alt.

Something to Think About

"The supreme fact for Paul was that he was a 'man in Christ.' It was by being 'in Christ' that a person could be justified before God and share the new life Jesus had come to bring. It was by being 'in Christ' that a person could die to sin and be raised to a new life, reconciled to God.

"For Paul, the fact that he was 'a man in Christ' was not just a theological theory. It was something that he had himself experienced. From the moment when he met the risen Christ on the Damascus road, Paul knew that his life was to be ruled, guided and directed by this new Lord whom he had previously despised. What Paul received from this Lord was not a system of ethics or doctrine, but rather a new life. It was a life that gave victory over sin and created a new fellowship in which all social and spiritual barriers were removed and overcome.

"Paul also discovered that because of his new relationship with God, he could enjoy a new freedom in his relationships with other people. It simply made no difference whether they were men or women, Jews or Gentiles, slaves or masters, educated or ignorant. Paul came to see that all people are of equal value to God.

"Paul is seen as a truly great man only when we view him as he saw himself: as 'a man in Christ.' He was a man who had denied himself in the most radical way possible, and for whom his risen Lord was everything: 'I count all things as loss because of the surpassing worth of knowing Christ Jesus my Lord' (Philippians 3:8, Revised Standard Version)."

John W. Drane, Paul: An Illustrated Documentary *(Harper and Row [Lion Publishing], 1976), 118, 120–21.*

Prayer

Lord Jesus, how can I ever thank You
for loving me the way You do?
I can be so stubborn, so self-righteous and proud.
Still You love me.
I can be so unwilling to listen, understand, and accept anyone different from me.
Still You love me.
I can be so rebellious, so eager to go my own way and follow my own course.
Still You love me.
You died for these sins. You forgive me freely.
Link me securely with all my brothers and sisters who love You and believe in You too.
Fill us with joy in diversity. Fill us with joy in unity.
For in You, dear Lord, we are one. Amen.

Digging Deep
My Personal Study for Week 7

The Holy Spirit builds the church. Beginning first in Jerusalem on Pentecost, on into Judea and Samaria by way of persecution, and then into all the Gentile world, the Good News of Jesus, the Savior, spreads and the church grows. Clearly Jesus, the head of His church, is in charge—choosing whomever He selects by His grace to build His church according to His plan.

Day 1 • Acts 9:1–9

1. Jesus predicted that the Gospel would be preached "to the ends of the earth." Saul is the unlikely convert Jesus chooses for this task. Write a thumbnail sketch of Saul (later known as the apostle Paul) from what you already learned about Saul in session 6 (question 3) and from the following passages: Acts 18:3; 21:39; 22:3; 23:16; 27–28; Galatians 1:13–14; Philippians 3:5–6.

2. Damascus, located about 150 miles from Jerusalem in the Roman province of Syria, was an independent city within the Nabatean kingdom (Arabia). Just before 130 B.C. a large group of Jews fled to Damascus, where they lived independently of the authorities in Jerusalem. Over the years these immigrants formed a large Jewish community with several synagogues. At first, persecuted Christians felt safe here. However, at this time the Roman government had given the Jewish high priest the right to extradite Jews outside Jerusalem. Paul was given those powers of extradition. Remember that these followers of "the Way" of the Lord, as Christians were called, were still Jews and subject to Jewish authorities in Jerusalem while the Romans were in power. Saul was persecuting Christians, not Jesus Himself. How, then, do you explain Jesus' words, "persecute Me" (v. 4)?

1 Corinthians 12:27

Ephesians 1:22–23

3. Compare Jesus' tone and approach to Paul with His approach to Martha and Jerusalem. How is God's grace evident in Jesus' encounter with Paul?

Acts 9:3–6

Luke 10:38–42

Luke 13:34–35

4. What do you think was going on within Saul during his first three days in Damascus (v. 9)?

5. *For personal reflection. Sharing optional.* When have you been stopped in your tracks and forced to spend time refocusing your life? With what results? How did God show His unconditional love (grace) at that time?

Day 2 • Read Acts 9:10–19

Perhaps the main character of this section is saintly Ananias, a Jewish Christian, well known and respected in the community. (Saul/Paul describes his encounter with him in Acts 22:12–16.)

6. *Ananias* is the Greek form of the Hebrew name *Hananiah,* which means "the Lord is gracious" or "the Lord shows grace." How does Ananias live up to his name as he relates to Saul?

The Church Affirms Gentile Converts as Equals with Jews

Distribute before session 8 for use in session 8.
Use enrichment magazine pp. 21–23.

Acts 9:32–10:48

Resources for Worship

Use these resources for your daily study at home and at the week's assembly.

Hymn

God of grace and God of glory,
On Your people pour Your pow'r;
Crown Your ancient church's story;
Bring its bud to glorious flow'r.
Grant us wisdom, grant us courage
For the facing of this hour.

Lo, the hosts of evil round us
Scorn the Christ, assail His ways!
From the fears that long have bound us
Free our hearts to faith and praise.
Grant us wisdom, grant us courage
For the living of these days.

Harry E. Fosdick

Something to Think About

In fervent gratitude for the Savior's dying love and His blood-bought gift of redemption, we dedicate ourselves to Him with all that we are and have; and in obedience to His call for workers in the harvest fields, we pledge Him our willing service wherever and whenever He hath need of us. We consecrate to our Savior our hands to work for Him, our feet to go on His errands, our voice to sing His praises, our lips to proclaim His redeeming love, our silver and our gold to extend His kingdom, our will to do His will, and every power of our life to the great task of bringing the lost and the erring into eternal fellowship with Him. Amen.

The Lutheran Women's Missionary League Pledge

Prayer

Lord Jesus, how wide and deep is Your love!

It searches to the ends of the earth for sinners of every kind and color, language, and tongue.

(That's why You found me.)

You died and rose and gathered us, my brothers and sisters and me, close to Yourself where there is love and peace.

Where have all those feelings gone,

those old feelings of distrust and indifference and fear and envy and hate?

You took them to the cross, Lord Jesus.

You gift us instead with mercy and tolerance and understanding and acceptance.

Now, as one, we live our lives in You.

What joy! Amen.

Digging Deep
My Personal Study for Week 8

The account of Peter's ministry picks up again. In this week's study we see Peter traveling from headquarters in Jerusalem throughout Judea, preaching and teaching in the many congregations that had sprung up after Pentecost. As he does so, the Lord prepares the way for the church to understand that the Gospel is for all people and not only primarily for Jews. Perhaps the other apostles also served as itinerant missionaries at this time. They have been witnesses for Christ "in Jerusalem, and in all Judea and Samaria," and now they will carry the Good News "to the ends of the earth" (Acts 1:8) to the first Gentile audience!

Day 1 • Read 9:32–43

1. During Peter's travels two miracles validate the truth of the apostle's teaching. The miracles did more than restore life to one person and set another on his feet.

a. What part did Peter play in these miracles (9:34, 40)?

b. What was the outcome (9:35, 42)?

2. a. In Acts 9:13 and 32 believers are called "saints." *Saint* means "holy" or "consecrated." How is it possible for sinful people to be called "saints"? (See 2 Corinthians 5:21.)

b. What comfort and challenge do you find in realizing that you are, at the same time, both sinner and saint?

3. Note what Acts 9:36 says about Dorcas. How does Dorcas illustrate James 2:18?

4. **Challenge question.** Note that Peter stayed in Joppa with a tanner named Simon (9:43). Since the work of tanners brought them into contact with the carcasses of dead animals, tanning was considered an unclean profession by scrupulous Jews (whose interpretation of such passages as Leviticus 11:39 went further than God's Law did). What does Peter's willingness to stay in the house of a tanner suggest about Peter's opinion of such scruples?

Day 2 • Read Acts 10:1–23a

The Lord brings Jews and Gentiles together in a way that makes plain His plan to bring Jews and Gentiles together in His church.

5. a. What do you learn from verses 1–2 about this "man named Cornelius"?

b. What does Cornelius have in common with the centurion and the Ethiopian official?

Luke 7:1–10

Acts 8:26–39

6. The dietary laws given to the Jews by God in the Old Testament were intended to set Israel apart and make it distinct from other nations. (You may read some of these laws in Deuteronomy 14:3–21.) Such laws emphasized the purity and self-discipline the Jews were to practice in their everyday living. Israel was consecrated as God's chosen instrument to bring the Savior into the world. Remembering this purpose of dietary laws would keep them in a right perspective.

a. What did Jesus say about clean and unclean foods in Mark 7:14–23?

b. How did Peter feel about the dietary laws (Acts 10:9–16)?

7. Just as Jews had an aversion to eating foods they considered unclean, so also they had an aversion to any contact with Gentiles. Strict Jews had little or no use for any Gentile. Some Jews even would refuse help to a Gentile woman in childbirth since this would only bring another Gentile into the world.

a. Read Isaiah 49:6. What was God's ultimate intention in the Old Testament regarding the relationship between Jews and Gentiles?

b. Peter was brought up with strict Jewish ideas both about eating unclean foods and about associating with Gentiles. How do you think God used the vision

The Church Thrives Despite Persecution

Distribute before session 9 for use in session 9.
Use enrichment magazine pp. 15–17.

Acts 11:1–12:25

Resources for Worship

Use these resources for your daily study at home and at the week's assembly.

Hymn

Speak, O Lord, Your servant listens,
Let Your Word to me come near;
Newborn life and spirit give me,
Let each promise still my fear.
Death's dread pow'r, its inward strife,
Wars against Your Word of life;
Fill me, Lord, with love's strong fervor
That I cling to You forever!

Precious Jesus, I entreat You,
Let Your words in me take root;
Let this gift of heav'n enrich me
So that I bring gen'rous fruit:
Never take them from my heart
Till I see You as You are,
When in heav'nly bliss and glory
I will meet You and adore You!

Anna Sophia of Hesse-Darmstadt; tr. George T. Rygh, alt.

Something to Think About

When a Christian begins to know Christ as his Lord and Savior, who has redeemed him from death, and is brought into His dominion and heritage, his heart is thoroughly permeated by God; then he would like to help everybody attain this blessedness. For he has no greater joy than the treasured knowledge of Christ. So he begins to teach and exhort others, confesses and commends his blessedness before everybody, and sighs and prays that they, too, may come to this grace. He has a restless spirit while enjoying rest supreme, that is, God's grace and peace. Therefore he cannot be quiet or idle but is forever struggling and striving with all his powers, as one living only to spread God's honor and praise farther among man, to cause others also to receive this spirit of grace and through it also to help him pray.

What Luther Says, *ed. Ewald Plass (St. Louis: Concordia Publishing House, 1959), § 3014.*

Prayer

Lord Jesus, thank You for Your Spirit, alive and at work within me and all Your children. Let the light of Your Spirit burn so brightly that everyone may see our Lord Jesus Christ reflected in what we say and what we do and how we do it. Let the light of Your Spirit burn so brightly that everyone may see our unity in You, our common commitment to sharing Your saving love, until, at last, Your kingdom comes. Amen.

Digging Deep
My Personal Study for Week 9

The church continues to grow among both Jews and Gentiles. Commitment and understanding of God's mission deepens. Although persecution arises again, it cannot stop the spread of God's Word.

Day 1 • Read Acts 11:1–18

1. Note the heart of the criticism of the "circumcised believers" (Jewish Christians), verse 3. Why was the kind of response Peter made to their criticism more effective than arguing or appealing to his own authority as leader in the church?

2. Perhaps the original manuscript for the Book of Acts was just the right length to fit on a 35-foot papyrus scroll. Considering all that Luke had to tell, why do you think he chose to include the account of Peter's experience with the Gentiles twice (Acts 10 and 11:5–15)?

3. What evidence do you see in verse 18 that the Holy Spirit is at work in the Jerusalem church?

4. a. Read Galatians 5:16–26. How was the fruit of the Spirit evident in the way the controversy over Peter's actions in Caesarea was settled?

b. If you can, tell about a time when you saw the Holy Spirit's influence at work in settling peacefully a controversy in your family or church.

Day 2 • Read Acts 11:19–30

Farther and farther the Good News about Jesus is shared. More and more people believe and turn to the Lord. Philip has preached to the Samaritans and the Ethiopian. Peter has preached to Cornelius and his household. Now for the first time believers from the island of Cyprus in the Mediterranean and from Cyrene in northern Africa deliberately preach the Gospel to Gentiles in Antioch! We don't know the names of these pioneers, but we do know God's power was mightily at work. The Lord was building His church.

5. a. Read verses 19–26. Antioch, 240 miles north of Jerusalem, was a city of half a million people in Luke's day. Built in 300 B.C., it was the third largest city in the Roman empire. Antioch was a cosmopolitan city of luxurious immorality centered on sport, gambling, and loose and lustful living. Review what you already know about Barnabas. (See Acts 4:36–37; 9:27.) Why do you think Barnabas was a good choice to visit Antioch on behalf of the church in Jerusalem?

b. *For personal reflection:* Who needs you to be a "Barnabas" today?

6. The name *Christian* means "belonging to Christ." It may have been a nickname coined by unbelieving Greeks to tease believers about their allegiance to Christ. It is used in verse 26 for the first time. Think about what it means to you personally that you belong to Christ. Finish this sentence, perhaps in several ways: "For me, belonging to Christ means I . . ."

7. a. Read verses 27–30. Here we find the first mention of the gift of prophecy in the Book of Acts. (See also Acts 13:1; 15:32; 19:6; 21:8–10.) The early church seems to have had three sets of leaders. Apostles exercised authority throughout the whole church. Elders (bishops, pastors), assisted by deacons, were the spiritual leaders of local congregations. Others, including prophets and evangelists, were not limited to one congregation. They preached, explained, or foretold under the direction of the Holy Spirit. Read verse 29. How can you, together with other Christians, respond to human need within the body of Christ, as these early Christians did? (Consider how this is done on a local, regional, and national level.) Notice that verse 29 indicates that the group decided how to help.

b. How might your LifeLight group reach out to fellow Christians in need?

Day 3 • Read Acts 12:1–5

Now begins a critical period for the church in Jerusalem. It is A.D. 41, about 10 years after Jesus' death and resurrection. Emperor Claudius replaced the Roman governor in Palestine with Herod Agrippa I, grandson of Herod the Great (who was in power at Jesus' birth). Although educated at Rome, Herod Agrippa was a Jew and eager to cultivate the good will of the Jewish people by keeping the law and traditional observances. Peter's conduct in the home of Cornelius would have outraged the Jews, and Herod Agrippa undoubtedly saw this as an opportunity to attack the apostles and increase his own popularity. What he hadn't counted on was the power of God to protect and strengthen His church—what he hadn't counted on was his own death.

8. a. Whom did Herod target?

b. What effect do you think this had on the believers in Jerusalem?

9. During the Week of Unleavened Bread (which began with Passover) no trial or execution could take place, according to Jewish law. How do you think Peter felt about the prospect of going on trial shortly after Passover? (Consider Matthew 26:1–4 as you answer.)

10. What thoughts, feelings, and petitions do you think were expressed in the earnest prayers of the church at this time?

11. How could you face death because of your faith?

1 Corinthians 15:55–57

2 Corinthians 12:9a

Hebrews 2:14–15

Day 4 • Read Acts 12:6–19

12. a. If you saw this account depicted on video, in a movie, or on the stage, what words might you use to describe it?

b. How might a Christian audience respond to what they saw?

13. Read verses 6–8. Herod may have heard of Peter's previous escape from prison (Acts 5:17–21). What precautions by Herod indicate that he considered Peter a prize prisoner?

14. Look back at your answer to question 11. How do these verses (6–8) describe Peter's disposition the night before his trial and probable execution?

15. a. Read verses 9–11. Dear Peter! Forever slow to catch on! How human he is! What does he finally understand?

b. Read verses 12–17. It is the middle of the night. Nevertheless, Peter goes straight to his friends, who are gathered at the home of John Mark's mother, Mary. Compare the activity in verse 12 with the words in verse 15. What's contradictory— and yet so human— about what's happening here?

c. *For personal reflection. Sharing optional.* Reread verse 11. What difficulty or burden in your life could be endured or lifted by this same understanding?

16. How do you think Peter's friends spent the rest of the night and the morning after his deliverance from prison?

Day 5 • Read Acts 12:20–25

Luke reports what happened three years after Peter's rescue. Peter had escaped, perhaps to Antioch. Herod Agrippa continued his lust for power and popularity. As this chapter of Acts comes to a close, Peter is alive; Herod is dead. And the Word of God continues to spread.

17. Herod Agrippa's quarrel with the Phoenician cities of Tyre and Sidon sets the stage for his downfall. Citizens from these cities depended on grain from Galilee. Herod may have placed an embargo on shipments. When a delegation came to beg for a settlement, Herod addressed them and a large crowd during a festival honoring Claudius Caesar. The Jewish historian Josephus reports that Herod wore a silver robe, which appeared to be dazzling bright in the light of the early morning sun. The crowd was impressed and shouted self-serving flattery, exclaiming that Herod was a god. Herod did not deny this, but basked in their blasphemy. He was overcome by intense pain, had to be carried out, and died five days later. In contrast to this detailed description of an enemy's death, note the succinct summary of the spread of God's Word and the growth of the church in verse 24. (Note previous summaries in 6:7 and 9:31.) From what you have learned so far, how would you account for this growth?

18. What do you see as your role in the ongoing spread of the Gospel?

19. How has this LifeLight study nourished your faith during the past nine weeks? List examples of truths you have learned and encouragement you've received that will help you in your daily Christian walk.

regarding unclean foods to prepare Peter to share the Gospel with Gentiles?

c. How can you tell that Peter was catching on to what the Lord was telling him (vv. 22–25, 27–28)?

8. *For personal reflection. Sharing optional.* Examine your own heart. Are you hiding feelings of aversion to some people? Do you sometimes feel superior or thank God that you are not like them? Read Luke 18:9–14 and James 2:10.

9. What can you do within your own church to break down hostility between races and classes of people?

Day 3 • Read Acts 10:23b–33

10. Peter and six friends from Joppa accompanied Cornelius's men to Caesarea. Both Cornelius and Peter acknowledged God's hand in bringing them together. What had Peter finally learned (v. 28)?

11. What do you think Peter meant when he said to Cornelius, "I am only a man myself" (v. 26)?

12. How did the experience Cornelius relates in verses 30–33 affirm the conclusion Peter had already drawn (vv. 34–35)?

13. In your opinion, what is most remarkable about Cornelius?

14. With whom do you identify more closely—with Peter or with Cornelius? Explain.

Day 4 • Read Acts 10:34–43

15. How does Peter explain what God has taught him (vv. 35–36)?

16. Peter reviews what his audience already knows (vv. 36–38) about Jesus. What did they still need to know (vv. 39–43)? Write down five or six main points you get from Peter's sermon.

17. a. What opportunities have you had to rub shoul-

ders or exchange a personal Christian witness with someone who may have had a racial or cultural background different from your own?

b. How have these experiences encouraged you or reinforced your faith or given you joy?

c. What will you do to carry God's gracious invitation to those outside your own culture and class?

Day 5 • Read Acts 10:44–48

God acts dramatically to make it clear that His kingdom is open to both Jew and Gentile.

18. Why might this episode be called "the Gentiles' Pentecost" (vv. 44–46)? See also Acts 11:15.

19. The Holy Spirit was creating faith in the hearts of those who listened as Peter preached the Gospel. Why do you think God poured out His Spirit in a visible sign (v. 45)?

20. a. How does Paul's statement in Galatians 3:26–29 harmonize with the events recorded in Acts 10:44–48?

b. What does your Baptism say about your relationship with baptized Christians who are different from you in respect to gender, economic or social status, or racial or ethnic background?

21. What do you think happened during the few days that Peter stayed with Cornelius?

7. a. How could you forgive someone who had threatened, abused, treated unjustly, harmed, or killed those you love?

Ephesians 4:32

Philippians 4:13

b. Why is accepting God's forgiveness crucial in learning to share forgiveness with others?

Matthew 6:14–15

Psalm 130:3–4

Ephesians 4:32

8. a. Read Acts 9:15–16. How were the Lord's plans for Saul/Paul fulfilled?

Romans 1:13–14

Acts 25:11–12

Acts 28:17

b. How did Saul/Paul suffer for the Lord (2 Corinthians 11:23b–28)?

c. What sustained Saul/Paul throughout his sufferings (2 Corinthians 12:9–10)?

Day 3 • Read Acts 9:20–22

9. In what ways was Saul/Paul's witness based on his own experience?

10. Read Saul/Paul's account in Galatians 1:15–24 of what happened after his conversion.

a. What facts does he add to the Acts account?

b. Why do you think a period by himself in Arabia would be important for Saul?

11. How might Saul feel now about the Christian believers whom he had earlier determined to hound to death?

Day 4 • Read Acts 9:23–25

12. Saul/Paul returned to Damascus from Arabia. He stayed in Damascus preaching like a second Stephen, trying to convince the Jews that Jesus is the Son of God and the promised Messiah. Why do you think his enemies (the Jews) would want to kill him?

13. God's grace intervened to save Saul (v. 25). Some of the houses built on the thick city wall had windows projecting over the wall. Saul probably went over the wall through one of these windows. Think of a time when the Lord provided a way out of danger for you. Thank and praise God for His deliverance as you recall that time. Be ready to tell your discussion group how it happened.

Day 5 • Read Acts 26–31

14. It was hard for the disciples in Jerusalem to forget what Saul/Paul had done.

a. **Challenge question.** What do you think there may have been about Barnabas that didn't hold Saul/Paul's past against him (Acts 4:36–37)?

b. Why did Peter and James finally accept Saul/Paul?

c. What does 1 Corinthians 13:1–7 say about our tendency to withhold forgiveness even when someone has changed?

d. How does the saying that "Christians aren't perfect, just forgiven" apply to Saul/Paul's situation and to our churches today?

15. Which verse or section in this week's study was most meaningful to you?

ward evidence of the Holy Spirit (similar to the Pentecost experience, Acts 2:4). How can we know that these believers had already received the indwelling of the Holy Spirit? Compare Acts 8:14 to 1 Corinthians 12:3. Compare Acts 8:16b to Acts 2:38.

b. As the apostles prayed, a special outpouring of the Holy Spirit came upon the Samaritans. Keeping in mind the racial tensions between the Jews and Samaritans, what do you think was the significance of this occurrence to the Samaritans? to the apostles?

Acts 10:45–46

1 Corinthians 12:12–13

9. The Holy Spirit works in various circumstances and ways. How and when did the gift of the Holy Spirit come in the following instances?

a. Acts 2:1–4

b. Acts 10:44–46

c. John 20:21–23

d. 2 Thessalonians 2:13–14

Day 4 • Read Acts 8:18–25

One Samaritan convert turned out to be quite controversial. The apostles' response to Simon the sorcerer shows their understanding of the mission God had given them and the gift He had graciously provided.

10. Review Acts 8:9–13, describing Simon the sorcerer's conversion. What do you think motivated Simon's request in verses 18–19?

11. Read Acts 8:13. Though Simon's conversion seems sincere, Peter's words to Him (8:20–24) contain a severe rebuke. What warning does this story have for church members today?

12. Review question 7 and read verse 25. How has John's attitude toward the Samaritans changed?

13. How do you account for this change?

Day 5 • Read 8:26–40

Another unusual convert is pictured in today's reading. Dramatically, God continues to provide opportunities for people of all races, places, and kinds to hear and respond to the Gospel.

14. God reaches people through people. God sets the stage and opens the doors. How is this true in this account?

15. The Ethiopian was probably one of a group called "God-fearers," Gentiles who were students of Judaism, attracted by its faith in one God and by its high moral and ethical teachings. God-fearers would often attend the synagogue and read the Jewish Scriptures. In contrast, proselytes were Gentiles who had been accepted fully into Judaism. They were circumcised and had taken upon themselves the responsibility of keeping the Law. Perhaps this Ethiopian had been denied the privilege of becoming a proselyte because of the physical mutilation that had made him a eunuch. (See Deuteronomy 23:1.) What evidence do you find in this account (in vv. 31–39) that the Ethiopian was drawn by the Gospel and was accepted fully into the Christian church?

16. Ethiopia very early became a stronghold of the Christian faith and still remains so today. What connection do you think there might be between that fact and this Ethiopian's conversion? (See v. 27.)

17. a. When has it seemed that God has put you in the right place, just at the right time?

b. *For personal reflection. Sharing optional.* What opportunities are available to you to invite someone to worship with you? to attend a LifeLight course? to share a Scripture portion or a prayer? to discuss the Christian faith and life? Pray for the Holy Spirit to lead you in making use of these opportunities.

Day 3 • Read Acts 7:1–38

In answer to the accusations against him, Stephen speaks at length, reviewing God's gracious dealings with His people. In his review of Scripture, he demonstrates their persistent refusal to receive God's saving work and Word.

7. Stephen reviews God's action on behalf of His people through Abraham, Joseph, and Moses. How did God bless His people through these patriarchs?

a. Abraham (vv. 2–8)

b. Joseph (vv. 9–15)

c. Moses (vv. 20–38)

8. What do you find in Stephen's speech that indicates the following points:

a. That God is not limited to one land and one temple (vv. 2, 9, 11, 29–30, 48–49)

b. That God's command is to "go out," not "stay put" (vv. 3, 12–15, 34)

c. That the people of Israel always rejected the leaders God sent (vv. 9, 25, 27, 35)

9. Stephen was challenging the council to be open to the truth, to repent, and to believe the witness of the Spirit to Jesus Christ as Savior for all the world. Why is it hard for Christians—and impossible for non-Christians—to do that?

John 3:6

Romans 8:7

Ephesians 4:20–24

1 Corinthians 2:14

10. When conflict over change arises, how should we work toward resolution? Let the following passages guide your answer.

a. Ephesians 4:26–27

b. 2 Timothy 3:16

c. James 1:19–20

d. 1 Peter 4:7–8

Day 4 • Read Acts 7:39–53

Stephen's speech to the council intensifies and comes home to his hearers!

11. Scan this section. List Stephen's accusations against the people of Israel—including these members of the

Sanhedrin. Try to find nine ways in which they have been unfaithful to God.

12. Stephen displayed courage as he spoke God's message to a hostile audience.

a. When have you needed courage to speak plainly about what you believe?

b. How can the following passages guide you in your approach to others?

Matthew 10:19–20

John 14:16–18

2 Corinthians 2:17

Ephesians 6:18

1 Peter 3:15–16

Day 5 • Read Acts 7:54–60

The Holy Spirit strengthens Stephen's witness to the Sanhedrin by revealing the glorified Jesus to him. Still the unbelievers refuse to see and to listen. Stephen makes the ultimate witness; he becomes the first Christian martyr.

13. Read verses 55–56, 59–60.

a. What evidence can you find that Stephen's witness was intended to call these sinners to repentance and faith?

b. How do you know that Stephen was on intimate terms with the Lord?

14. **Challenge question.** See the references below, noting how Jesus used this psalm before His enemies and this very Sanhedrin. What features of these texts, when related to Stephen's vision, should have terrified this Sanhedrin and brought them to repentance?

Matthew 22:41–45

Matthew 25:31

Matthew 26:64

Psalm 110:1

15. Today some Christians may not be threatened with death for their witness to Christ, though many are. Yet Christians may die "little deaths" each day when their choices, values, and lifestyle clash with those of the world or when they attempt to share God's Word honestly.

a. When have you died "little deaths"?

b. Why have you been able to rejoice at such times (Romans 5:3–6)?

Galatians 6:7–8

examine your own motives in worship. Then speak to God about them—in words of confession and thanksgiving, asking Him for His Spirit to enable you to grow in heartfelt worship.

Day 3 • Read Acts 5:12–16

8. Read verses 12–16. We learn a great deal about the church in these few verses. What significance do you see in the following?

a. the apostles performed miracles and wonders
Mark 16:15–20

Acts 8:6

b. the believers met openly in the temple
Luke 12:4–5

Acts 5:29

c. half-hearted "followers" stayed away
Acts 5:11, 13

d. the number of true believers continued to grow
Acts 5:14

Romans 1:16

e. *For personal reflection. Sharing optional.* Prayerfully

9. Notice in 5:14 and in many passages in Acts (8:3, 12; 9:2; 16:1, 13–14; 17:4, 12, 34; 18:2; 21:5) that Luke makes a point of noting the presence and participation of women with men within the Christian fellowship.

a. What point is being made about the matter of gender among Christians in these texts and in Galatians 3:28?

b. How does this reality affect you personally?

Day 4 • Read Acts 5:17–26

10. How do you think the congregation reacted when all of its leaders were imprisoned?

11. How do you know, from verses 20–21, that the apostles clearly understood their identity as witnesses for Christ?

12. How does this account show that the church is the Lord's and not a human institution?

13. God's miracles are always full of purpose.

a. Why were the apostles released from prison?

Verse 20

Verse 24

b. From what have you been "released" and for what purpose?

Day 5 • Read Acts 5:27–42

14. a. What was the high priest's "agenda" in his approach to the apostles (v. 28)?

b. Compare this to Peter's "agenda."

Verse 29

Verse 32

15. **Challenge question.** Read verse 33. The Sanhedrin was "furious" at Peter's witness and wanted the apostles put to death. Refer to Acts 2:37. Why do you think this group remained blind to the evidence while others believed?

Matthew 23:23–28

2 Corinthians 4:4

16. a. Read the following verses and write a definition of "faith."

John 3:16

Romans 3:21–26

Hebrews 11:1

Ephesians 2:8–10

b. What are some ways we in our LifeLight group might encourage a more faithful witness to Jesus— in our own lives and in our congregation?

17. Do you think Gamaliel was a friend or foe of the apostles? Explain.

18. Which verse or section in this week's study was most meaningful to you and why?

10. God was at work in the healing of the crippled man so Jesus might be glorified and the disciples might have an opportunity to tell others about the grace and love of Jesus. Has God similarly given you golden opportunities to tell others about the grace and love of Jesus? If so, choose one of these that you remember and tell the others in your study group about it.

Day 3 • Read Acts 3:11–26

11. a. Compare Peter's speech to the onlookers (vv. 12–26) to his Pentecost sermon in Acts 2:14–39. Find common elements—for example, What specific sin(s) of his hearers does he point to? (Note the accusatory "you.")

b. What was *God's* action in response to their sinful deed(s) (v. 15)?

c. How may the hearers receive forgiveness?

12. Imagine Peter speaking directly to you. Which words or phrases in Peter's sermon are especially meaningful to you and why?

13. Note (vv. 12–13) that Peter and John give God the glory for what they've done. Think about a time when someone praised or thanked you for something you did. How did or could you have witnessed by giving glory to God?

14. Most Bible versions (e.g., KJV, NASB, RSV, NKJV, ESV, NET) translate verse 21 as "Whom heaven must receive." This is more accurate than the NIV translation, "He must remain in heaven." How does this verse and also Matthew 28:20; Acts 1:11; Ephesians 1:20–23; Colossians 2:9; and Revelation 1:7 support or contradict the following summary statement: The one person, Jesus Christ, both according to His divine and His human nature, is invisibly but actually present everywhere now. When He "comes again" at the end of the world, everyone will see Him.

Day 4 • Read Acts 4:1–22

15. What can we learn from verses 1–7 about the Sanhedrin's attitude toward Peter and John?

16. Read verses 8–12. Review your answer to number 8 under Session 2. How does Peter's answer to the Sanhedrin reflect his earlier witness?

17. Read verses 13–21. What deciding factors determined the Sanhedrin's recourse in this matter?

18. a. Note that Jesus Himself in John 14:6 and John 3:36 confirms Peter's words in Acts 4:12. Yet as many as 40 percent of churchgoers agree with the following survey statements: "Salvation depends on being sincere in whatever you believe"; "Although there are many religions in the world, most of them lead to the same God"; "God is satisfied if a person lives the best life he or she can." Think about other such statements you have heard—or with which you have been tempted to agree. In your opinion, what is it that leads people to rely on such "homemade" religions?

Romans 10:3–9

Galatians 3:1–2, 10–11

b. How would (or did) you answer someone who expressed such a works-righteous faith?

19. Note that Peter simply spoke "filled with the Holy Spirit" (v. 8). See Jesus' promise in Matthew 10:19–20. Tell about a time when the Holy Spirit gave *you* words to say in a difficult or frightening situation.

20. Consider the apostles' words to the authorities in 4:18–20 and 5:27–29 and also Paul's advice in Romans 13:1 and Titus 3:1. Write a summary statement indicating when it is right or wrong to obey or disobey authorities whom God has placed over us.

Day 5 • Read Acts 4:23–31

21. **Challenge question.** Write a brief prayer that puts the thoughts expressed in verses 24–30 in the context of our own times.

22. **Challenge question.** Match the words of the Psalm 2 quote from Acts 4:25–26 to its fulfillment.

Psalm	New Testament Fulfillment
"nations"	______________
"peoples"	______________
"kings of the earth"	______________
"rulers"	______________
"Anointed One"	______________

23. a. Note verse 29. What "threats" does the church face today as it seeks to witness about Christ to the world?

b. What "threats" and discouragements do you face personally?

c. What encouragement does this section of Scripture and the experience of the early church give you as you prayerfully consider speaking the "word of God boldly"?

24. How might a Christian congregation and/or a larger group of Christians in a church denomination speak the Gospel about Jesus with greater boldness? (Suggest some specific ideas.)

25. In the privacy of your individual study time and then in your discussion group, pray that the Lord might give us, individually and in our congregations and larger church body, a greater boldness in proclaiming the Gospel.

7. Read verse 20 and Jesus' fuller description in Matthew 24:29–31. Note the ultimate horrors to be seen and felt in the sun and moon just before the Last Day. Why can we actually *look forward* with joy to that day?

Luke 21:28

Acts 2:21

Day 3 • Read Acts 2:22–36

Peter continues his preaching, personalizing the message, outlining God's plan of salvation, quoting David's prophecy, testifying to Christ's resurrection, explaining the outpouring of the Spirit, claiming Jesus as Lord and Messiah.

8. In appealing to his Jewish listeners, why do you think it was essential that Peter witness to Jesus' crucifixion as well as to His resurrection?

Isaiah 53:2–10

Psalm 16:8–11

9. a. How are *you* responsible for Jesus' death on the cross (Romans 3:9–18)?

b. How are *you* affected by His resurrection (1 Corinthians 15:17–23)?

Day 4 • Read Acts 2:37–39

10. Peter's preaching got results. List them.

11. How does Peter appeal to his listeners in verses 38 and 39?

12. What gifts did you receive in your Baptism?

Acts 2:38

Acts 22:16

Romans 6:3, 5

Titus 3:4–7

13. *For personal reflection. Sharing optional.* Romans 6:1–14 reveals what our Baptism indicates or means for our everyday life. Slowly, thoughtfully, prayerfully read these verses. Breathe a prayer to the Spirit to make more real to you the wonder and beauty of your union with Christ through your Baptism. Then "bury" or "drown" your old sinful flesh by confessing to God your Father your sins and failings this day. And then claim for yourself again the wonderful forgiveness you have through Christ's resurrection. In the joy of that forgiveness "count [yourself] dead to sin but alive to God in Christ Jesus" . . . and "offer [yourself] to God" as one who has "been brought from death to life."

Day 5 • Read Acts 2:40–41

14. a. What means did (and does) God use to call sinners to Himself? See also 1 Corinthians 1:21 and Romans 10:8–17.

b. What evidence of the *power* of the Spirit do you see in verse 41?

15. a. What opportunities have you had this week to tell in your own words the story of sin and grace?

b. Who or what helped you in your telling?

c. What would increase your confidence?

16. Which verse or section in this week's study has been especially meaningful to you? Why?

His Spirit in your life. Confess any misdirected priorities. Claim the forgiveness Jesus won for you. Read Romans 8:12–17 and reflect on what the power of His Spirit enables you to be and to do.

Day 3 • Read Acts 1:9–11

At a definite moment in time Jesus came into the world. At a definite moment in time He removed His visible presence. At a definite moment in time He will visibly return. Until then, His disciples are to work at the task He has assigned to them.

9. **Challenge question.** Acts 1:9–11 describes Jesus' ascension into heaven. Why did Jesus return to heaven?

Ephesians 1:22–23

John 16:5–8

Day 4 • Read Acts 1:12–14

10. What significance do you find in the fact that the disciples returned to the room where they were staying together and there prayed with other believers (v. 14)?

11. How do their actions reveal their acceptance of Jesus' authority (v. 4)?

12. Note Acts 1:14 and John 7:5. What do you think accounts for the change we see in Jesus' brothers?

13. a. *For personal reflection. Sharing optional.* Although the disciples were promised that the Holy Spirit would come to them, they had to undergo a period of waiting (vv. 4, 14). Is there some area of your own life where you are waiting upon the Lord? If so, consider whether you might share this information with your discussion group and pray with them about it.

b. How has the experience of waiting upon the Lord in the fellowship of other Christians strengthened you in your own spiritual journey?

Day 5 • Read Acts 1:15–26

In the Book of Acts many speeches show how the church grew and developed. Note the speech made by Peter in this section.

14. What was Peter's purpose in addressing his fellow believers (vv. 16–22)?

15. What can we learn from Peter about what to rely on in setting a course of action?

v. 20

v. 24

16. What qualifications were required of those nominated to fill the office left vacant by Judas (vv. 21–22)?

17. All offices and duties to be performed in the Old Testament temple were chosen by lot. Names of candidates were written on stones, which were put into a vessel and shaken. The name on the first stone to fall out of the vessel was elected. What is the relevance of Proverbs 16:33 to the selection of Matthias to fill the place of Judas?

18. The 120 Christians in Jerusalem at the time referred to in our reading today represented one Christian for every 30,000 others in Palestine.

a. Nevertheless, what effect did this small band of witnesses have?

Acts 2:47

Acts 4:4

Acts 5:14

Acts 6:7

b. Do you ever see yourself as in a tiny minority as you witness for Jesus? If so, how does this make you feel?

19. Which verse or section has been most meaningful to you this week?